SCHOOL BUS

DONALD CREWS

For the buses, the riders, and the watchers

ISBN 0-590-44153-1

 Published by Scholastic Inc., 730 Broadway, New York, NY 10003, by arrangement with Puffin Books, a division of Viking Penguin Inc.

35 34 33 32 31 30 29 4 5 6 / 0

Printed in the U.S.A. 08

First Scholastic printing, September 1990

SCHOLASTIC INC.
New York Toronto London Auckland Sydney

SCHOOL BUS
SCHOOL BUS
SCHOOL BUS
SCHOOL BUS
SCHOOL BUS
SCHOOL BUS
SCHOOL BUS
SCHOOL BUS
SCHOOL BUS
SCHOOL BUS
SCHOOL BUS
SCHOOL BUS
SCHOOL BUS
SCHOOL BUS
SCHOOL BUS
SCHOOL BUS

Yellow school buses

SCHOOL BUS

large and small.

Empty yellow buses cross the town.

84 BKLYN
SCHOOL BUS
STOP
ON SIGNAL
WAL~MART
SCHOOL BUS

STOP.

WAL~MART
TAXI

GO.

WALK
SCHOOL BUS
STOP
ON SIGNAL

Going this way.

Going that way.

Here it comes.

WAL~MART

SCHOOL
BUS
STOP
WAL~MART

See you later.

Full buses head for school.

SCHOOL BUS
SCHOOLBUS
SCHOOL BUS

SCHOOL BUS
SCHOOL
STOP
ON SIGNAL

Here we are.

SCHOOL

Right on time.

SCHOOL BUS
SCHOOL BUS
SCHOOL BUS

Empty buses wait.

School's over.

SCHOOL BUS
WAL~MART
SCHOOL BUS
SCHOOL BUS

SCHOOL BUS
SCHOOL BUS

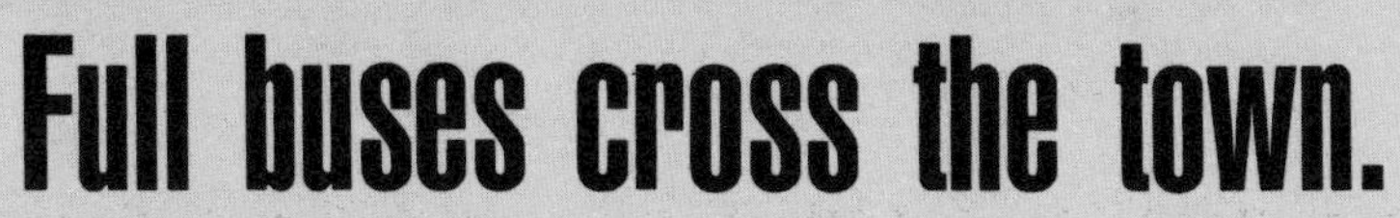

Full buses cross the town.

SCHOOL BUS
STOP

Home again.

SCHOOL BUS
SCHOOL BUS
SCHOOL BUS
SCHOOL BUS
SCHOOL BUS
SCHOOL BUS
SCHOOL BUS
SCHOOL BUS
SCHOOL BUS
SCHOOL BUS
SCHOOL BUS
SCHOOL BUS
SCHOOL BUS
STOP
ON SIGNAL
SCHOOL BUS
STOP
ON SIGNAL
SCHOOL BUS
STOP
ON SIGNAL
SCHOOL BUS
STOP
ON SIGNAL

Home again.